INTRODUCT[illegible]

For a great many years the steam roller at work on the highways of t[illegible] ht, so much so that they were often not given a second glance by the publi[illegible] of steam engine which were in general commercial use, a number were in fac[illegible] However, by the fifties and sixties the writing was on the wall - many were lying [illegible] [cont]ractors and council yards, others were to be found standing at the side of minor roads and in lay bys.

As the interest in steam power was already well under way at this time, many of those once unwanted engines were available for purchase at very reasonable prices, resulting in the large number of rollers which have survived into preservation, many now in a condition equal, if not better externally, than which they originally left the works.

Careful study of engine sale reports during the early sixties reveal some interesting facts. For instance a sale at a contractors yard, where twenty Aveling & Porter rollers were offered for sale, all except one in working order. The lowest figure paid was for a 1929 10 ton roller was £120!, most went for amounts under £200, while three made £250 each! Steam rollers could be purchased at this time for even lower figures. Very different to the prices that they change hands for these days, even allowing for inflation.

One company which developed and built steam rollers over a great many years, having several proven and popular designs was Aveling & Porter, the oldest known surviving roller in the UK built by the company dating back to 1882, while the most recent Aveling Barford survivor was built in 1948. A large number of Aveling rollers have survived into preservation. Indeed it would be very rare to attend an engine event and not find at least one Aveling present.

Many other companies also catered for this very lucrative market, which existed both at home and overseas. Among these are many interesting designs which include vertical and inclined boiler designs, Tandem and Tri-tandems, to name just a few. Indeed, a considerable number of roller designs, all adding variety to the range of engine types to be seen in this country.

This title, a further album in the 'Vintage Steam' series, adds an important section of the engine designs to those already covered, which are ploughing engines, agricultural, tractors, showmans locomotives and road locomotives; others are planned in the series which will build up to a very representative selection of preserved steam engines.

Below: This interesting rally archive photograph of Burrell class A roller no. 3047 was taken nearly thirty years ago. No. 3047 is among the oldest Burrell rollers to survive into preservation, being built at Thetford in October 1908, the oldest known survivor dating back to 1904. This engine is a double crank compound of 6NHP and weighing 10 tons.

1. Only two rollers built by Wm. Allchin Limited of 'Globe Works' Northampton have survived into preservation, both of which were owned by Northampton Borough Council. This one is works number 1187, a ten ton roller built in 1901, and is a single cylinder 6 NHP design.

2. Seven rollers built by Armstrong Whitworth remain, this one is works number 10R2, the oldest of the survivors, built in 1923. The engine is a 5 NHP ten ton compound and was owned by Kettering Council, Northamptonshire.

3. Aveling Barford built this single cylinder roller, works number AC606, in 1937, a 6 NHP ten ton design.. This low angle shot shows the scarifier and the name on the canopy, Eddison.

4. Another of the rollers built in post war years is this Aveling Barford six ton roller works number AG757, a 4 NHP single cylinder design, ten rollers built by this company from 1946 onwards survive in preservation. Aveling Barford was the result of the amalgamation of the road roller building interests of Aveling & Porter of Rochester, and Barford & Perkins of Peterborough following the collapse of the Agricultural and General Engineers combine in the 1930s.

5. A fine example of a post war Aveling Barford roller, works number AH 162 a single cylinder 6NHP ten ton model built in 1948 and supplied new to the Great Western Railway at Paddington, later passing to Coles of Bristol. The roller is at present preserved in Cornwall. These post war rollers were actually built for Aveling Barford by Ruston & Hornsby, as the Grantham works had turned over completely to diesel roller production.

6. Aveling & Porter number 3586 was built in 1895, a fine example of the 8NHP fifteen ton design, when new the roller was supplied to Sefton Rural District Council (Liverpool), later passing into the ownership of the Lancashire Road Rolling Company and on to Cardigan Council in 1927, where it remained until 1960.

7. This fine Aveling & Porter, single cylinder, ten ton roller is among the oldest survivors being built in 1889. Works number 2481 was supplied new to the Cambridge Improvement Commissioners, later passing into the ownership of Cambridge City Corporation.

8. The fate of both these collectors items is not known, fortunately the Aveling & Porter roller survives, it is works number 4232 built in 1898, a 5NHP compound twelve ton design. When photographed in 1961 it was standing on the roadside at Betts-y-Coed North Wales awaiting its next job.

9. During its working life this Aveling & Porter 5NHP ten ton roller , works number 4505 worked in several parts of the country. Built in 1900 the roller was supplied new to Christchurch Rural District Council Hampshire. In 1910 it returned to the builders as a part exchange deal, bring resold to Bomford & Evershed, later passing to an owner in Cumberland.

10. This rear view of Aveling & Porter six and a half ton Tandem roller, number 6530, built in 1908, shows clearly the layout of the rolls and footplate controls on this quite distinct design. Tandem rollers were introduced on the scene when asphalt surfacing came into vogue.

11. Aveling & Porter type R15 fifteen ton roller was built in 1906. The engine is a 7 NHP compound works number 6090, being supplied new to Beverley Urban District Council and later passing on to the East Riding Council.

12. This ten ton Aveling & Porter roller was supplied new to Eddisons of Dorchester and later passing in to the ownership of Surrey County Council. The roller is works number 7771, built in 1912, it is a 5NHP single cylinder design.

13. Aveling & Porter developed several designs over the many years that they built rollers, this engine is an example of the class MLD 'Shay Drive' of which only ten were built. This one, number 7411, built in 1912 being the sole survivor. It was supplied new to Fulham Borough Council, London. The 'quick reverse' action of the Shay type engine prevented 'dwell' when rolling hot asphalt.

14. This typical Aveling & Porter twelve ton roller left the works in 1919, carrying works number 9027 the roller is a 5 NHP compound design, and is seen here in this 1973 photograph complete with scarifying equipment.

15. For a great many years this Aveling & Porter twelve ton roller stood at the roadside near Spaldwick, Huntingdon. Works number 8918 built in 1918, was one of the lucky ones as it was rescued for preservation, after a very long exposure to the elements.

16. Aveling & Porter 5 NHP single cylinder roller number 9024 was supplied new to Shropshire County Council in 1919. This roller has been in preservation for forty years.

17. This unique Aveling & Porter roller started its working life as a tractor for Kent County Council. In 1934 it was converted to a roller by Allens of Oxford, it is thought to be their only roller conversion surviving, note the company name on the casting near the chimney. The works number of this eight ton roller is 11423, built in 1926 it was supplied new as mentioned above, on conversion to a roller it was purchased by Wingham Engineering.

18. This roller is typical of many that were to be seen on the highways of this country up until the mid sixties. Aveling, works number 12442 was built in 1929 and is a 7 NHP single cylinder design.

19. Now superbly restored this Aveling & Porter single cylinder ten ton roller was supplied new to the well known West Country contractors W. W. Buncombe of Highbridge Somerset where it was their 'number 41'. The works number of the roller is 10596 being built in 1923.

20. Aveling & Porter 3 NHP six ton roller seen here with the rear rolls and driving controls clearly shown. This roller is works number 11556, built in 1926, a single cylinder design this engine spent much of its working life in London before being owned by Taylor Bros. of Wimbish, Essex.

21. Aveling & Porter rollers are usually to be found at most rallies, which is not surprising as a great many are in preservation. Many rollers due to transportation difficulties only attend events in their immediate vicinity. This one is a fine example, preserved in Leicestershire, being works number 12468, a 4 NHP eight ton compound, built in 1929.

22. Babcock & Wilcox roller number 95/4013 was built in 1926 and supplied new to W W Buncombe & Sons of Highbridge Somerset, and was still used by the company up to the early sixties. All five Babcock rollers were built by Clayton & Shuttleworth Ltd., the company being absorbed by Babcock & Wilcox Ltd., in 1924. Babcocks later disposed of Clayton & Shuttleworth to Marshalls of Gainsborough, in 1929.

23. Another view of Babcock & Wilcox roller number 95/4013, this time showing the flywheel side, note the chimney cap carried on a hook at the side of the front roll.

24. This interesting photograph shows two Burrell ten ton rollers built in 1924 side by side once again. Both were supplied new to R Dingle & Sons, Stoke Climsland, Cornwall, one, number 3999 (nearest camera) remaining in the county where it is still preserved, the other number 3991 was sold to an owner in the Home Counties.

25. The entire working life of this Burrell roller was spent in the ownership of Doran Bros. of Thetford, Norfolk. Burrell works number 3994 was built in 1924 and is a 5 NHP eight ton design. The engine is now preserved in the county in which it was built and worked.

26. Burrell compound eight ton roller number 4067 built in 1927 seen here at Harewood House in 1964. When new this 4 NHP roller was supplied to G. Hall of Kirkburton, Huddersfield.

27. This fine example of the Burrell fourteen ton design was built in 1927 being a 6 NHP single cylinder design, works number 4070. The roller was still owned by J Dickinson & Sons (Emley) Ltd. Doncaster when this photograph was taken in 1967. The company having owned the roller since new, and used it with others in their fleet extensively in Yorkshire.

28. The Burrell number 4070 as it is at the present time, having changed hands and moved south during the early 1980s. This roller is one of the last built at the famous Thetford works.

29. Burrell works number 4083 was the last roller built by the company, it was supplied in 1928 to East Suffolk County Council. The roller has since been converted to a tractor. This photograph showing the engine as it was in 1971.

30. Clayton & Shuttleworth of Lincoln built this single cylinder 4 NHP ten ton roller in 1914 as works number 46688. When new it was supplied to John Peter Jones & Son of Newtown, later owners were the Buttington Road Rolling Co. of Welshpool.

Plate 1. This nostalgic photograph depicts a once very familiar sight on the highway. Fowler number 21698 was still hard at work in Mid Wales when the photograph was taken. Fortunately this 12 ton class DNC roller built in 1937 has survived into preservation.

Plate 2. Only ten of these 'Shay Drive' Aveling & Porter class MLD rollers were built, number 7411 was built in 1912 and is the sole survivor. This Tandem, quick reverse roller, weighs 6 tons and was supplied new to Fulham Borough Council London for who it worked until the late 1920's.

Plate 3. This fine 10 ton Clayton & Shuttleworth roller was built in 1923, it is a single cylinder design with the works number 48751. The roller was supplied new to W W Bumcombe of Highbridge Somerset, well known road contractors.

Plate 4. This superbly restored example of the Wallis & Steevens 'Advance' design roller was built at Basingstoke in 1923 as works number 7784. Quite a considerable number of this design roller have survived into preservation.

Plate 5. When new this Fowler 5NHP 10 ton class DNB compound roller was supplied to Midlothian County Council. The roller was built at Leeds in 1927 as works number 17501.

Plate 6. Marshall 10 ton roller, works number 71833 was built at Gainsborough in 1919. Marshall rollers were very popular with road contractors and County Councils.

Plate 7. *Seven rollers built by Armstrong Whitworth Ltd. are known to survive, this one, works number 10R 2, built in 1923 is the oldest survivor, it is a 10 ton 5NHP compound roller, all the survivors are 10 ton models with the exception of one 12 ton design.*

Plate 8. *This 10 ton 6NHP piston valve 2 speed Aveling-Barford roller was built in 1937 as works number AC606. The last surviving steam roller built by this company was an 8 ton model built in 1948.*

31. Eleven rollers built by Clayton & Shuttleworth of Lincoln are thought to be in preservation, this one built in 1925 is the youngest of those that survive. The engine is works number 48971,a single cylinder ten ton design.

32. Fowlers of Leeds were well known for their rollers, this one is a fine example of the class DN compound built in 1927 as works number 17077. This ten ton roller was supplied new to P. Dillon of Limerick, but later returned to Fowlers and was resold to Mechanical Spraying & Grouting Co. Ltd. of Reading Berkshire.

33. A large number of rollers built by Fowlers are in preservation, among them is works number 17501, a class DNB ten ton compound built in 1927 for Midlothian County Council, later passing to W. H. McAlpine.

34. Years of hard work were showing on this 1929 Fowler, works number 17586 when photographed at the roadside near Barmouth in 1963. It would appear that the roller is one which has not survived although somehow it may have escaped the fate which befell so many. The Bedford lorry in the background would also now be a collectors item.

35. This Fowler 5 NHP class DNA single cylinder ten ton roller spent its entire working life with Kitcheners of Potton Bedfordshire. The engine is works number 17560 being built at Leeds in 1929. This fine roller has been in preservation for over thirty years.

36. This fine example of the Fowler DNB class was built at Leeds in 1930 as works number 18659. The engine is a single cylinder design weighing twelve tons. This photograph was taken in 1990 and clearly shows many hours of careful restoration.

37. Very few Garrett rollers have survived into preservation, this one number 34267, was built in 1924. The engine is a 5 NHP compound, the rollers did not generally enjoy the popularity of the 4CD tractors.

38. Another roller which was part of the Paisley collection was this Marshall eight ton roller, works number 61307, built in 1913. The engine is a two speed single cylinder model which was at the time of the sale fitted with an 'Allen Patent Scarifier' for scarifying road surfaces.

39. This Marshall eight ton roller has attended events for many years and is a superb example of the Marshall 'S type' design, number 76116 is a 4 NHP engine. Note the Marshall insignia on the cylinder block and 'Britannia' emblem on the headstock, together with the crest on the motion cover.

40. This Marshall S type roller spent its working life in Portugal. Identification of the engine is difficult as all plates have long since disappeared. It is thought to be number 78787 built in 1925/26, verification is expected as the roller is dismantled for restoration which is now under way. In spite of general appearance the condition of the boiler. firebox and bearings is good.

41. This superbly restored Marshall Q class, works number 76797 is a 5 NHP single cylinder ten ton roller was built at Gainsborough in 1923.

42. Marshall U class (Universal) roller number 85060 was built in 1929. Very few examples of this design remain, this engine being a 5 NHP eight ton unit. During its working life the roller was owned by Ilford Council and used on tarmacadam work. This type was Britannia Works' answer to the Wallis & Steevens 'Advance' type.

43. This Marshall Q class ten ton roller was originally owned by Lindsey County Council Lincolnshire. Works number 76796 was built in 1923 being a single cylinder 5 NHP design, it is one of several members of this class built in that year to survive into preservation.

44. Only seven of this type of Marshall Tandem rollers were produced, with five of those being exported. Marshalls introduced the design for easy manoeuvrability and direction change without 'dwell', among the features are steam steering and instant reverse. Details of this very interesting ten ton vertical boiler roller are works number 87125 built in 1933, being supplied new to Norwich Corporation.

45. Another view of Marshall works number 87125 showing the other side of this interesting vertical boiler roller. Note the Marshall crest above the front roll. Very few vertical boiler rollers are in existence.

46. Marshall Universal ten ton roller number 87635 was built at Gainsborough in 1935, spending its entire working life with West Sussex County Council, being fleet number 49. This 5 NHP design has enclosed motion. Several rollers were still to be found at work in the sixties including this fine Marshall. The separate steam offtake for the cylinders reduced the chance of 'priming' when engaged in quick reverse work on asphalt, caused by the water surging to and fro in the boiler.

47. Another very interesting roller design is the Robey 'Tri-Tandem'. This one was at work until the late sixties being owned by Wirksworth Quarries Ltd. having been used in many parts of the country. Robey & Co of Lincoln built this roller in 1930 as works number 44083, the engine is a two speed double crank compound, it was converted to 'Tri-Tandem' in the mid 1930s. Robey tandem rollers were based on that firms wagon design of boiler and motion.

48. Robey 'Tri-Tandem' roller number 45655 was built in 1930 and also supplied new to Wirksworth Quarries Ltd. working for the company until 1963. During the rollers working life it had been used on several motorway building programmes.

49. Ruston & Hornsby 5 NHP roller works number 149813 was built in 1928, being an example of the SR class ten ton model. The roller was sold via. Ransomes, Sims & Jefferies of Ipswich and to Claytons contractors of Coltishall Norfolk, after five years it was resold to Messrs Plumbly & Gaze.

50. Another view of Ruston Hornsby number 149813, this time showing the flywheel side. Nine rollers built by this company survive in the British Isles.

51. Ruston & Proctor of Lincoln built this ten ton class SCR roller in 1915. The company Ruston Proctor and Richard Hornsby & Sons Ltd. of Grantham amalgamated in 1918 to become Ruston Hornsby Ltd. The works number of this 6 NHP roller is 50735 being supplied new to Louth Corporation Lincolnshire, after twenty years it was acquired by a private contractor.

52. Very few rollers built by Taskers of Andover Hampshire remain. This one, works number 1933 was built at the 'Waterloo Ironworks' in 1926, being a type C 6 NHP ten ton unit. This roller is now part of the Tasker Trust which is in the care of the Hampshire County Council.

53. One of the oldest surviving Wallis & Steevens rollers is this one, works number 2574, built at Basingstoke in 1902. The engine is a single cylinder ten ton design. A large number of the surviving Wallis rollers are of the 'Advance' type.

54. This neat three ton Wallis & Steevens roller was built at Basingstoke in 1903, starting its working life as a tractor owned by J & G Miller of Mitcham Surrey. In 1912 it was returned to the works where it was converted to a roller spending much of its later working life in Radnorshire Wales. The works number of the smart roller is number 2660, being a three NHP single cylinder engine.

55. Wallis & Steevens built a large number of rollers in several designs. This ten ton 5 NHP compound model is works number 7742 being built at Basingstoke in 1921, and supplied new to Southampton City Council where it spent its working life.

56. This Wallis & Steevens 'Simplicity' roller number 7939 built in 1927, was exhibited at the Public Works Roads & Transport Exhibition Islington London in November of that year and was supplied after the event to E. W. Parry of Putney London, later passing into the ownership a plant hire company.

57. Before - Wallis & Steevens 'Advance' six ton roller, works number 7784 stands in the line of engines awaiting the auctioneers attention at the Paisley collection sale on the 1st. October 1980. The roller was complete and certainly in need of restoration.

58. After - The same roller ten years later this photograph shows the roller superbly restored in August 1990. Number 7784 was built in 1923 and was owned by Wirksworth Quarries being purchased for preservation in 1961.

59. The Wallis & Steevens 'Simplicity' 1 NHP three ton roller was designed for export mainly to the Far East, only fifteen examples were built, many of which stayed in this country, six having survived into preservation. This one in the photograph is works number 7981 being built in 1930 and supplied to Thomas C White of Guildford Surrey.

60. Wallis & Steevens 'Advance' ten ton roller, works number 7931 was built at Basingstoke in 1927. The roller looking rather unusual without a canopy when the archive photograph was taken in 1967.

61. The Wallis & Steevens 'Advance' design roller was in production for many years. This low angle shot of number 8096 built in 1935, shows clearly the detail of this carefully restored ten ton roller which was supplied new to Barry Council in South Wales.

62. The last Wallis & Steevens 'Advance' roller Built and thought to survive is works number 8112 built in 1939 it was supplied new to Pontypridd Council. The 'Advance' design were very popular and a considerable number are in preservation, this engine is a 5 NHP eight ton design.